VOCAL SELECTIONS

RODGERS AND HAMMERSTEIN

Oklahoma!

Applications for performance of this work, whether legitimate, stock,
amateur, or foreign, should be addressed to:
RODGERS & HAMMERSTEIN LIBRARY
1633 Broadway
New York, NY 10019

ISBN 0-88188-099-X

WILLIAMSON MUSIC™
A RODGERS AND HAMMERSTEIN COMPANY

Exclusively Distributed by
HL Hal Leonard Publishing Corporation
7777 West Bluemound Road P.O. Box 13819 Milwaukee, WI 53213

OH, WHAT A BEAUTIFUL MORNIN'

Lyrics by OSCAR HAMMERSTEIN II
Music by RICHARD RODGERS

* *Names of chords for Ukulele and Banjo.*
Symbols for Guitar.

I CAIN'T SAY NO!

Lyrics by OSCAR HAMMERSTEIN II
Music by RICHARD RODGERS

men. I know I must-n't fall in-to the pit,—— But when I'm with a fel-ler, I fer-

Lively

git!

Refrain

I'm jist a girl who cain't say no, I'm in a tur-ri-ble
I'm jist a girl who cain't say no, Cain't seem to say it at

sempre marcato

fix —— I al - ways say "come on, le's go"
all —— I hate to dis - ser - point a beau

THE SURREY WITH THE FRINGE ON TOP

Lyrics by OSCAR HAMMERSTEIN II
Music by RICHARD RODGERS

*Names of chords for Ukulele and Banjo.
Symbols for Guitar.

KANSAS CITY

Lyrics by OSCAR HAMMERSTEIN II
Music by RICHARD RODGERS

MANY A NEW DAY

Lyrics by OSCAR HAMMERSTEIN II
Music by RICHARD RODGERS

Why should a wo-man who is health-y and strong, Blub-ber like a ba-by if her man goes a-way? A - weep-in' and a-wail-in' how he done her wrong, That's one thing you'll nev-er hear me say! Nev-er gon-na' think that the

*Names of chords for Ukulele and Banjo
Symbols for Guitar

PEOPLE WILL SAY WE'RE IN LOVE

Lyrics by OSCAR HAMMERSTEIN II
Music by RICHARD RODGERS

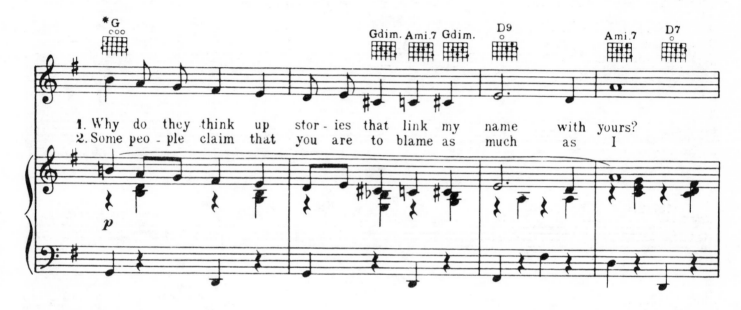

1. Why do they think up stor-ies that link my name with yours?
2. Some peo-ple claim that you are to blame as much as I

Why do the neigh-bors chat-ter all day, be - hind their doors?
Why do you take the troub-le to bake my fav' - rite pie?

* *Names of chords for Ukulele and Banjo.*
Symbols for Guitar.

OUT OF MY DREAMS

Lyrics by OSCAR HAMMERSTEIN II
Music by RICHARD RODGERS

Names of chords for Ukulele and Banjo.
Symbols for Guitar.

THE FARMER AND THE COWMAN

Lyrics by OSCAR HAMMERSTEIN II
Music by RICHARD RODGERS

good! _____ I don't say I'm no bet-ter than an-y-bod-y

else, But I'll be damned if I ain't jist as good! _____

Ter-ri-to-ry folks should stick to-geth-er, Ter-ri-to-ry folks should all be pals,

Cow-boys dance with the farm-ers' daugh-ters, Farm-ers dance with the ranch-ers' gals!

OKLAHOMA

Lyrics by OSCAR HAMMERSTEIN
Music by RICHARD RODGERS

Brand new state! Brand new state, gon-na treat you great! ___ Gon-na give you bar-ley, car-rots and per-ta-ters, Pas-ture fer the cat-tle, Spin-ach and ter-may-ters! Flow-ers on the prair-ie where the June bugs zoom, Plen'-y of air and

* *Names of chords for Ukulele and Banjo.*
Symbols for Guitar.

ALL ER NOTHIN'

Lyrics by OSCAR HAMMERSTEIN II
Music by RICHARD RODGERS

ese pages are excerpted from

HE RODGERS & HAMMERSTEIN FACT BOOK,

etailed 806-page book edited by Stanley Green, covering the work of both dgers & Hammerstein. Available through Hal Leonard Books #00183656.

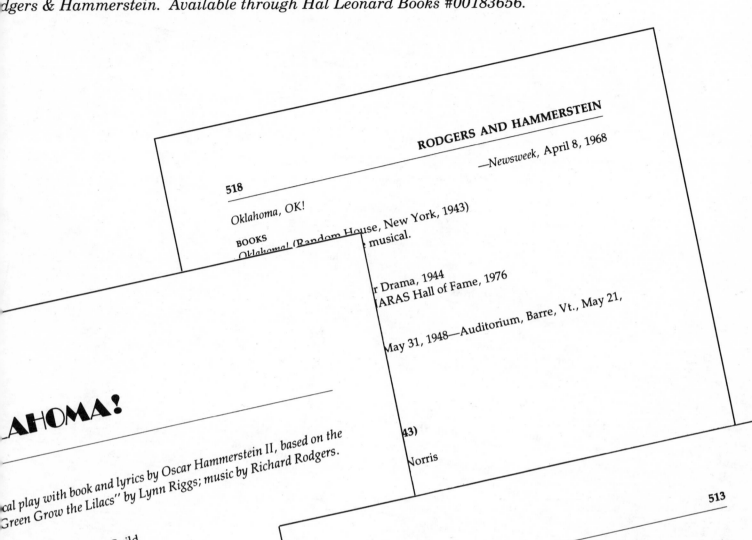

RODGERS AND HAMMERSTEIN

—*Newsweek*, April 8, 1968

518

Oklahoma, OK!

BOOKS
Oklahoma! (Random House, New York, 1943)
musical.

r Drama, 1944
ARAS Hall of Fame, 1976

May 31, 1948—Auditorium, Barre, Vt., May 21,

43)

Norris

513

OKLAHOMA!

Musical Numbers
The action takes place in Indian territory (now Oklahoma), just after the turn of the century.

ACT I
SCENE ONE—THE FRONT OF LAUREY'S FARMHOUSE
Oh, What a Beautiful Mornin', CURLY
The Surrey With the Fringe on Top, CURLY, LAUREY, AUNT ELLER
Kansas City, WILL, with AUNT ELLER and BOYS
I Cain't Say No, ADO ANNIE
Many a New Day, LAUREY and GIRLS; danced by SYLVIE, ARMINA, ELLEN
It's a Scandal! It's a Outrage!, ALI HAKIM and BOYS and GIRLS
People Will Say We're in Love, CURLY and LAUREY

SCENE TWO—THE SMOKE HOUSE
Pore Jud Is Daid, CURLY and JUD
Lonely Room, JUD

SCENE THREE—A GROVE ON LAUREY'S FARM
Out of My Dreams, LAUREY and GIRLS
Laurey Makes Up Her Mind Ballet
LAUREY, Katharine Sergava
CURLY, Marc Platt
JUD, George Church
THE CHILD, Bambi Linn
JUD'S POST CARDS: Joan McCracken, Kate Friedlich, Margit DeKo
LAUREY'S FRIENDS: Rhoda Hoffman, Rosemary Schaeffer, Nona
Maria Harriton, Diana Adams, Billie Zay
COWBOYS: Gary Fleming, Erik Kristen, Jack Dunphy, Ray Harri
Kenneth LeRoy, Eddie Howland, Kenneth Buffet
OST CARDS: Bobby Barrentine, Vivian Smith

AHOMA!

cal play with book and lyrics by Oscar Hammerstein II, based on the
Green Grow the Lilacs" by Lynn Riggs; music by Richard Rodgers.

ented by the Theatre Guild
cted by Rouben Mamoulian
reography by Agnes de Mille
tings by Lemuel Ayers
stumes by Miles White
usic director, Jacob Schwartzdorf (Jay S. Blackton)
Orchestrations by Robert Russell Bennett
Production supervised by Theresa Helburn and Lawrence

Tryout
(known as "Away We Go!")
Shubert Theatre, New Haven, March 11-13, 1943
Colonial Theatre, Boston, March 15-27, 1943

New York Run
St. James Theatre, March 31, 1943-May 29, 1948 (five years
2,212 performances (including 44 special matinees for the ar
NOTE: For fifteen years—from July 1, 1946 through July 11, 1961—O
record as the longest-running musical in Broadway history.

The Story
In the days of the Oklahoma land rush, both Jud F
ranch hands, are in love with Laurey. Although it i
whom she loves, Laurey spites him by going to a da
There, Curly proves his love by bidding all he own
food basket. They marry, and after the ceremony, Ju
with Curly and is killed by his own knife. Curly is ac
spot.

The Cast
AUNT ELLER MURPHY, Betty Garde
AIN, Alfred Drake
Roberts

OKLAHOMA!

IKE SKIDMORE, Thomas Spencer
FRED, Elliott Martin
SLIM, William Sutherland
WILL PARKER, Walter Donahue

danced by Remington Olmstead, Jr.)
...othea MacFarland
...lheim
...eline Daniels

...elson
...n S. McCarthy
...ence
...ad, Jr.

...d, Marjorie Austin, Elise Klingerman, Marianne
...hart, Margot Moser, Isabel Bigley, Brender Barker,
...Walter Peterson, Robert Patterson, Elliot Martin,
...omason, Earl Young, Peter Evans

RODGERS AND HAMMERSTEIN

...yriska Teater, Göteborg, Sweden, Sept. 29, 1950
Directed by Egon Kjerrman; choreography by Svenäge Larsen. Cast: Arne Hasselblad (CURLY); Berit Kjerrman (LAUREY); Maj Lindström (ADO ANNIE); Jackie Söderman (WILL); Märta Ternstedt (ELLER); Claes Jakobsson (JUD); Rutger Nygren (ALI).

Théatre des Champs-Elysées, Paris, June 20-July 3, 1955
ANTA "Salute to France" production; directed by Rouben Mamoulian; choreography by Agnes de Mille. Cast: Jack Cassidy (CURLY); Shirley Jones (LAUREY); Pamela Britton (ADO ANNIE); Harrison Muller (WILL); Edith Gresham (ELLER); C. K. Alexander (ALI); Clark Winters (JUD). Tour: Rome, Naples, Milan, Venice, July 9-August 16, 1955.

Takarazuka Theatre, Tokyo, September 2-26, 1967
Presented by the Takarazuka Revue Co.; translated by Iwao Mori and Hideyuki Kawai; directed and choreography reproduced b... Lappe. Cast: Noboru Kozuki (CURLY); Jun Hatzukase (LA... Yashioji (ADO ANNIE); Harumi Suga (WILL); Tamamo Mizus... Harumi Yaye (ALI); Miyako Koshiro (JUD). Note: This was a... company.

OKLAHOMA!

(London Production—1947)

Presented by H. M. Tennent Ltd.
Restaged by Jerome Whyte
Miss de Mille's choreography reproduced by Gemze de Lapp...
Settings by Lemuel Ayers
Costumes by Miles White
Music director, Salvatore Dell'Isola
Orchestrations by Robert Russell Bennett

London Run

Theatre Royal, Drury Lane, April 29, 1947-May 27, 1950
Stoll Theatre, May 29-October 21, 1950
1,548 *performances*

NOTE: Until it was overtaken by *My Fair Lady* on January 10, 1962, O... Lane, which first opened its doors in 1663.

1,380 performances, was the longest-running production in the hi...

The Cast

AUNT ELLER MURPHY, Mary Marlo
...Y MCLAIN, Harold (Howard) Keel (danced by Erik Kriste...
Betty Jane Watson (danced by Gemze de ...

OKLAHOMA!

"Oklahoma!" Closes in London after 3½ Years Stay with Gross
Take of $4,300,000
—*Variety*, Octobe...

OKLAHOMA!

(Film Version—1955)

Distributed by Magna Theatre Corporation
Presented by Messrs. Rodgers and Hammerstein
Produced by Arthur Hornblow, Jr.
Directed by Fred Zinnemann
Screenplay by Sonya Levien and William Ludwig
Choreography by Agnes de Mille
Production designed by Oliver Smith
Costumes by Orry Kelly and Motley
Production aide, John Fearnley
Music director, Jay Blackton
Orchestrations by Robert Russell Bennett
Background music adapted by Adolph Deutsch
Photographed by Robert Surtees
Editor, Gene Ruggiero
Filmed in Todd-AO
Color by Eastman Color

Release Date

October 11, 1955

NOTE: On November 1, 1956, the film was rereleased by... shown in Cinemascope.

The Cast

...CURLY MCLAIN, Gordon MacRae (danced by Ja...
...NES, Gloria Grahame (danced by B...